a Question of Courage

(14)

OXFORD *Playscripts*

● ●

Series Editor – Bill Lucas

adapted by Bill Lucas and
Brian Keaney

Marjorie Darke

a Question of Courage

Oxford University Press

Oxford University Press, Walton Street, Oxford OX2 6DP

Oxford New York Toronto
Delhi Bombay Calcutta Madras Karachi
Petaling Jaya Singapore Hong Kong Tokyo
Nairobi Dar es Salaam Cape Town
Melbourne Auckland

and associated companies in
Berlin Ibadan

Oxford is a trade mark of Oxford University Press

Original novel **A Question of Courage**
© Marjorie Darke 1975
This adaptation © Bill Lucas and Brian Keaney 1990
Reprinted 1991
This collection © Oxford University Press 1990
Activities in this collection © Bill Lucas 1990

A CIP catalogue record for this book is available from
the British Library

ISBN 0 19 831271 7

Typeset by Times Graphics

Printed in Great Britain at the University Press, Cambridge

Contents

Page

Characters 6

The Play: A Question of Courage 8
Act One 9
Act Two 39

Activities
The Suffragettes 72
Prison Diary 78
Women Today 82
Making a Protest 83
Drama Ideas 86
Peter and Emily 88
What the Adaptors Say 90
Designing a Set 91
A Question of Courage on Stage 92

Acknowledgements 94

Characters

In order of their
appearance on
stage.

Mrs Harris	*A dressmaker who employs Emily and Vera in Birmingham.*
Ada **Alice** **Flo**	*Girls who work for Mrs Harris.*
Vera Bradshaw	*One of the girls employed by Mrs Harris; Emily Palmer's friend.*
Emily Palmer	*The heroine of the play, employed by Mrs Harris*
Mrs Craig	*One of Mrs Harris' customers.*
Louise Marshall	*A strong-headed, well-to-do young suffragette.*
Neighbour	*Mrs Nailor's neighbour.*
Mrs Nailor	*A secondhand dealer who likes her gin.*
Ernie Palmer	*Emily's very religious brother.*
Mrs Palmer	*Emily's mother.*
Mr Palmer	*Emily's father.*
May Palmer	*Emily's younger sister who is disabled.*
Vic Palmer	*Emily's jolly brother.*
Boys	*Neighbours of the Palmers.*
Peter Marshall	*Louise Marshall's brother, a carefree soul.*
Woman	*Neighbour of the Palmers.*
Mrs Boddington	*The Vicar's wife and a supporter of the suffrage movement.*
Woman	*A suffrage movement supporter.*
Josiah Marshall	*A businessman, father of Louise and Peter.*
Maid	*The Marshalls' maid.*

Una and Maude Holiday	*Supporters of the suffrage movement.*
Constable	*Policeman in Birmingham.*
Keeper	*Gamekeeper at golf course.*
Mrs Silver	*A dressmaker in London's Soho who employs Emily and Vera.*
Mary Grant	*A leading supporter of the suffrage movement.*
Chairman	*The chairman of the Liberal Party meeting.*
Policeman	*A policeman in the magistrate's court.*
Wardresses	*In Holloway Prison for women.*
Doctor	*In Holloway Prison.*
Dr Curtis	*Doctor who attends Emily.*

The Play
· · · · · · · · · · · · · ·

The play is set in Birmingham and in London in the years leading up to the outbreak of the First World War in 1914.

Act One
....

Scene One

*Mrs Harris's shop. **Emily Palmer** and four other girls are machining and stitching. **Mrs Harris** is putting the final touches to **Mrs Craig**'s hem, while at the same time managing to keep an eye on the girls. The doorbell rings.*

Mrs Harris   Go and see who that is, Emily. I'm only halfway round Mrs Craig's hem. Don't know who it can be at this time of day, I'm sure. There's no more fittings and only half an hour before we close.

Ada   *(Nudging **Emily** who is daydreaming)* Emmie wake up! Ma 'Arris is talking to you.

Emily Palmer   What's that?

Mrs Harris   Emily Palmer, stir yourself! I don't pay you to daydream. Go and see who's at the door. If it's a customer, show her into the parlour.

Emily goes out onto the front of the stage where we imagine the parlour to be.

Louise Marshall   Good afternoon! Mrs Harris is expecting me. Tell her Miss Louise Marshall is here.

Emily is staring half-admiringly, half-enviously.

Well, aren't you going to tell your mistress I'm here?

Emily Palmer   Mrs Harris said for yo to wait in the parlour. I'll tell her yo're here.

*Emily rushes back into the shop, almost knocking over **Mrs Craig**.*

Mrs Harris   Miss Palmer, really!

Emily Palmer	I'm sorry, Mrs Craig. A young lady to see yo, Mrs Harris, Miss Louise Marshall.
Mrs Harris	Get back to your work then. Well, Mrs Craig, I think we're finished.
Mrs Craig	Thank you, Mrs Harris.
Mrs Harris	I'll just see you to the door.

*She sees **Mrs Craig** out, then goes to meet **Louise Marshall.***

Ada	She's all of a do-dah. Who was it?
Emily Palmer	Oh, I don't know, some stuck up miss.
Alice	Go on, tell us!
Ada	Don't be so aggravating, Emmie. Who was it?
Emily Palmer	Said her name was Louise Marshall, *(imitating her accent)* Miss Louise Marshall.

Vera looks up from her work at the name.

Someone yo knows?

Vera shakes her head.

Flo	Yo're a turn, Emmie.
Mrs Harris	*(From front stage)* Bring me that bolt of green silk out here, Emily.
Vera Bradshaw	In favour today, Emmie.
Emily Palmer	Bloomin' slave yo means. *(She pulls vigorously at a roll of cloth and in the process manages to rip it.)* Bloody thing! It would be today of all days. She knows I want to go on time to pick up my new bicycle.
Mrs Harris	Hurry up, girl.

Emily Palmer	Coming, Mrs Harris. *(To the girls)* Silly old cow.

Emily rushes out trailing green silk.

· ·

Scene Two

*The street outside **Mrs Nailor**'s house. Enter **Emily**, breathless.*

Emily Palmer	*(Shouts)* Mrs Nailor! Mrs Nailor!
Neighbour	No use calling 'er, duck. She's down the pub drinking this week's 'ousekeeping and the week after's.
Emily Palmer	I'll try down there then.
Neighbour	Yo the girl that's been coming these past ten Saturdays?
Emily Palmer	Yes.
Neighbour	I'll tell 'er yo've been here. What name is it?
Emily Palmer	It don't matter.

She turns to go.

*Enter **Mrs Nailor**, coughing.*

Mrs Nailor	Just come at the right moment, ain't I?
Emily Palmer	Please, Mrs Nailor, I've come for the bicycle.
Mrs Nailor	What's the rush, lovie?
Emily Palmer	I've got to get back home, or mam'll skin me.
Mrs Nailor	Oh all right then. Gimme that one and a tanner.

*Emily hands coins to **Mrs Nailor**, who counts them, then exits.*

Neighbour	Same story every week. Soon as she gets a penny off yo, she's off down the shop like greased lightning. No borrowing a screw of tea then. It's 'alf a pound and a lardy cake as like as not.
Emily Palmer	She's taking her time. I hope she ain't gone off to the pub again.
Neighbour	Well if she 'as, yo won't see 'er no more tonight. Spend it all on gin.

*Enter **Mrs Nailor**, wheeling a bicycle.*

Emily Palmer	*(Running her hands over bicycle)* It's really mine at last.
Mrs Nailor	Take it, duck. Yo deserve it.

∙∙∙

Scene Three

*The kitchen of the Palmer house. **Mrs Palmer** is cooking breakfast. **Emily** is ironing her brothers' shirts while the rest of the family gradually arrives. **Ernie Palmer** enters, part-dressed for church.*

Ernie Palmer	I'm starved! *(He puts his boots down and sits at the table.)* Where's my stiff collar, Mam?
Mrs Palmer	Emmie, get it out of the drawer.
Emily Palmer	Why can't he get it himself?
Mrs Palmer	Do as yo're told, girl.

Mr Palmer enters the kitchen looking hung-over and points at the collar Emily is ironing.

Mr Palmer	Shan't be wanting that. Tell your Mam I'm not coming to church.

He leaves abruptly.

May Palmer	*(Entering the kitchen and pulling Emily to the front of the stage)* Is the bike all right, Emmie, have yo looked?
Emily Palmer	How should I know? *(Looking angrily at the ironing)* I've not had a chance to look. But it's sure to be safe, dry enough too. Vic's sacks will have kept out the rain.
May Palmer	Will you try it soon?
Emily Palmer	Not yet. Put your foot in here.

> *Emily helps **May** into her thick leather leg irons.*

Tell yo what, first chance we get I'll give yo a ride. I'll hold yo safe and yo're small enough for your legs not to get in the way of the pedals.

May Palmer	Oo, Emmie, will yo?
Emily Palmer	Yo first, then me.

> *Vic **Palmer** enters loudly and grabbing **Emily** by the waist spins her round and kisses her affectionately on both cheeks. Her other brother, **Ernie**, starts reading a religious pamphlet at the table.*

Emily Palmer	*(Laughing)* Mam, Dad isn't coming to church.
Mrs Palmer	Oh isn't he ? We'll see about that. The very idea! As if it weren't bad enough my eldest son following the devil's beckoning finger, preaching Satan's words on street corners. *(To **Ernie**)* Oh, yo can shrug your shoulders, my lad, but when Judgement Day comes it won't be your name that the angels call. I've spent my life trying to push yo into the ways of righteousness, but yo're as pig-headed as most men and more so than some.
Mr Palmer	*(Returning to the kitchen)* Stop that bloody nagging! It's getting so a man can't be master in his own house.

Mrs Palmer   If yo was to act proper there'd be no need for me to speak up.
                    Ernie learns his heathen ways from yo. There's nothing to
                    choose between the pair of yo. Where's your dignity and
                    principles?

Mr Palmer   Shut up, woman! Yo gets worse every day. Woman isn't to fling
                    her weight about. Bad as them Suffragettes gabbing all the time
                    about principles and such stuff. Go and join 'em if yo likes.
                    Throw a few bombs, burn a few houses, smash a few windows.
                    It'll maybe get rid of your bad temper and give us some peace.

Mrs Palmer   Don't yo dare class me with them hussies. I'm a God-fearing
                    woman and don't yo forget it. I wouldn't have anything to do
                    with that lot if my life depended on it.

Mr Palmer   Gab on if yo likes, I'm not agoing.

                                        He leaves the kitchen. **Mrs Palmer** *stands
                                        shaking her head at* **Emily**.

· ·

Scene Four   *The road behind the Palmer house.*

May Palmer   Can we go now? Is it safe?

Emily Palmer   I think so. *(**Emily** wheels her bike on stage.)* Come on then.

May Palmer   Can I?

                                        Emily *helps* **May** *into the saddle with
                                        great difficulty and wheels her around the
                                        stage.*

Emily Palmer   My turn now.

                                        Emily *wobbles her way off stage.* **Two boys**
                                        arrive to watch. **Emily** *wobbles her way
                                        back on to the stage.*

Boy   Bony Emmie, bony Emmie, where's yo bloomers gone?

With obvious satisfaction **Emily** *puts two fingers in the air at the boy as she disappears off-stage.*

....

Scene Five

Further down the road. **Emily** *is lying on the ground with her bicycle.* **Louise** *and* **Peter Marshall** *are bending over her.*

Louise Marshall   Please, are you all right ?

Emily Palmer   *(Clearly dazed)* Miss Louise Marshall . . . my bicycle, is it . . .

Louise Marshall   No bones broken I hope. We simply couldn't help hitting you. One moment nothing, the next there you were straight in our path and not a chance of cutting round you. I'm terribly sorry.

Emily Palmer   My bicycle?

Peter Marshall   Her heart's in the right place, Lou, concerned more for her machine than her bruises. It's a bit twisted. Nothing that can't be put right.

A crowd is beginning to form.

Louise Marshall   Things before people again, Peter! For goodness sake give me a hand, can't you?

Peter Marshall	Keep calm, Lou. One thing at a time.
Louise Marshall	How do you expect me to keep calm when we are going to be late? We've cut it pretty fine as it is.
Woman	There'll be a bobby 'ere soon. Got noses fer trouble, bobbies.
Louise Marshall	Oh Lord, do something, Pete, or we'll be here for ever.
Peter Marshall	Righty-ho. Who's being callous now?

> *Peter picks up the bicycle to put it on the roof of his car.*

Emily Palmer	Hey, what are yo doing with my bike?
Peter Marshall	Putting it on the roof, of course.
Louise Marshall	Oh, come on, Peter. *(To Emily)* Sorry and all that. I'm sure you don't mind doing a round trip, but I simply can't be late for the meeting. Peter'll fix your bicycle. He's a splendid mechanic.
Emily Palmer	Where are we going?
Louise Marshall	What?
Emily Palmer	Where are yo taking me?
Louise Marshall	To the meeting, of course. The Women's Suffrage meeting. You know, Votes for Women. Come on.

• •

Scene Six

The drawing room of the Boddingtons' home (the Vicarage). Chairs are arranged and people are arriving for a meeting. At one side of the stage there are two chairs on a small raised platform for the speakers. In front of the two chairs there is a small table with a velvet cloth and a carafe of water. Emily is sitting two seats away from Vera.

Vera Bradshaw	I never thought to see you here. Never in this wide world.
Emily Palmer	Yo're not the only one to get a surprise.
Vera Bradshaw	How did you come to hear of the meeting?
Emily Palmer	By accident. *(**Louise Marshall** walks past the girls up onto the platform.)* I came with her.
Vera Bradshaw	Who?
Emily Palmer	Louise Marshall.
Vera Bradshaw	But you never let on you knew her at work.
Emily Palmer	I didn't then. She knocked me off my bicycle. Or at least this fellow who was driving the car did.
Vera Bradshaw	That's her brother. Brings her to all the Women's Suffrage meetings, collects her too.
Emily Palmer	I thought they was called Suffragettes.
Vera Bradshaw	No, they're different.
Emily Palmer	What's the difference?
Vera Bradshaw	Don't you read nothing? I'd have thought you'd take an interest.
Emily Palmer	Oh, don't be so sniffy!
Vera Bradshaw	We make our protest without violence. Suffragettes smash windows and burn houses, things like that.
Mrs Boddington	*(Clapping her hands)* Ladies, quiet please. Would you be seated. I think there are enough chairs. As you know, this meeting is a new venture for the working women in this area of Birmingham. The National Union of, er, Women's Social Suffrage is, er, helping to widen our horizons. Our speaker, Miss Marshall, is, er, going to address us on the subject of, sisters less, er, fortunate than ourselves.

Louise Marshall	Thank you, Mrs Boddington. It heartens me to see how many care for our cause, heartens me even more to see new faces. I particularly appreciate the effort you have all made in coming here. Women have so many duties and so few spare moments. We are all here because of our concern about the degrading position we are forced to accept in daily life. This is to be an appeal to you all to join with us in the fight for Justice and the Vote. It is 1912, my friends, yet for half the population of Great Britain we might still be in the Middle Ages. Rich and poor we are chained together and branded as *women*, inferior creatures without brains. And who brands us so? Men! *(Leaning forward and looking hard at the faces of the men in the audience)* There are women all over England banding together in a variety of groups to fight this injustice.
Woman	What can we do about it then?
Louise Marshall	We can demonstrate. We can use petitions, go on marches, chain ourselves to railings, interrupt political meetings, refuse to pay taxes, smash windows. I could go on and on. We women may equal men in number, but do we have equivalent rights? You know without me telling you that the answer is no, *(banging the table)* no, no!

> *There is applause from the audience, some shouting of agreement and questions about what is to be done.*

As to how you can help, I would urge you to seize every opportunity to talk and explain our cause. From tiny specks of dust, mountains are made and mountains are strong and we women are strong.

> *The audience cheers.*

Louise Marshall	May I go on to suggest an idea I've borrowed from other members of our movement: a bicycle parade with placards secured to each machine. We could . . .
Mrs Boddington	A bicycle parade?

Louise Marshall   Yes, a bicycle parade, Mrs Boddington. I have three machines
and can borrow two others. Perhaps some of you are cycling
enthusiasts and would like to join the outing. I was going to
suggest it might take place next Sunday afternoon. Anyone who
would like to know more, perhaps would see me while we have
the cups of tea our hostess has generously offered to provide.
And thank you all, thank you.

*After a moment's silence there is loud
clapping with many of the women getting
to their feet.*

Emily Palmer   This parade sounds interesting. I'm going to find out more about
it. Are yo coming?

She walks to the platform, followed by
Vera.

Louise Marshall   *(Pleased to move away from* **Mrs Boddington** *who is looking
distinctly unhappy)* You will come on the parade, won't you? I
know you have a bicycle.

Emily Palmer   It's damaged.

Louise Marshall   It's all right, you know. Pete's top hole with machines. You'll see
when you come to our house next Sunday for the parade. It'll be
as good as new, better even. Say you'll come.

Emily Palmer   Well . . .

Louise Marshall   You will, won't you?

Emily Palmer   All right.

Louise Marshall   Splendid, and you, Miss Bradshaw?

Vera Bradshaw   I've got no bicycle.

Louise Marshall   Then you can borrow one of mine. That's settled. Three o'clock
shall we say, next Sunday? We'll start from my house in
Hardwick. I haven't quite worked out the route. A round trip, I
think. We'll take a picnic. It'll be great fun.

Mrs Boddington	Oh, Miss Marshall, about the, er, bicycle parade. Before you go any further with it, I felt I, er, must ask if you really think that . . . are you sure it's the right thing . . .
Louise Marshall	It's all arranged, Mrs Boddington. Three o'clock next Sunday, from the Tower House. We'll be expecting you!

> *Mrs **Boddington** turns sharply and disappears, clearly annoyed.*

Emily Palmer	Yo coming, Vera?
Vera Bradshaw	*(Drinking a cup of tea)* Not yet.
Emily Palmer	See yo tomorrer then.

> *She starts to leave, moving towards the front of the stage.*

Peter Marshall	I say, wait a minute! Aren't you coming with us?
Emily Palmer	It's all right. I'm walking.
Peter Marshall	But you're limping.

> *Emily nods.*

I've had a quick look over your bike. I've straightened the handlebars and Gardiner's mending the puncture this very minute. A dab or two of paint and you'll never know anything happened.

Emily Palmer	Oh thanks!
Peter Marshall	Lou's still talking I suppose?

> *Emily nods.*

What did you think of it?

Emily Palmer	It was very interesting.

Peter Marshall	You've been bitten then ? Filled with enthusiasm against all those fiendish men! Women for ever . . .
Emily Palmer	Miss Marshall talked a lot of sense.
Peter Marshall	She would certainly talk a lot!
Emily Palmer	They was true them things she said. Women will have to stay at the kitchen sink unless something's done.
Peter Marshall	I'm only joking really. Lou knows how to twist words. She's a born wheedler and I pull her leg about it. It's a good thing really, this Women's Suffrage lark. Let's get Lou and then I'll get Gardiner to bring the car round.

They exit together.

. . . .

Scene Seven

*The kitchen of the Palmer house. **Vic** is sitting at the table drinking tea. **Mrs Palmer** is standing on one side of the stage with a dish cloth in one hand. She is clearly just outside the kitchen. Enter **Emily**. The first part of the scene is played outside the kitchen, then the action moves inside.*

Mrs Palmer	Yo all right, girlie?

***Emily** freezes and her mother catches her, firmly holding her with an arm around her shoulders.*

Yo little devil! Frightening the life out of us. We thought yo was dead. *(Slapping her across the cheek)* That's for all the trouble yo caused. *(Slapping her a second time)* And that's for making an indecent show of yourself, riding a bicycle on the Lord's Day.

Emily Palmer	But, Mam . . .

***May** enters quietly.*

Mrs Palmer	And where yo been ever since? *(Hitting her again)* Willie Green came with tales about yo scandalising the street showing your legs. Then our Ernie says Joe Nailor saw yo knocked down by a motor car. *(**Mrs Palmer** raises her hand to strike **Emily** once more.)*
May Palmer	Oh don't, Mam, don't.
Mrs Palmer	I'll thump yo an all, missie.
Mr Palmer	*(From off-stage)* Wheer's that bloody little tart ?

He enters and walks unsteadily towards **Emily,** *about to hit her.*

Vic Palmer	Leave her alone.
Mr Palmer	Yo keep out of it.
Vic Palmer	Only if yo gives over.
Mr Palmer	God damn it.

*Vic hits his father hard on the nose before he has time to react. **May** screams.*

Mrs Palmer	I'll not have yo two scrapping on the Lord's Day.

She goes to try and break up the fight.

Vic Palmer	Get out of it Emmie, run.

Emily runs off stage.

Mr Palmer	*(Shouting)* Hear me, girl? If I ketch yo going with a fancy man agin, I'll swing for yo. Are yo listening, m'girl?

Scene Eight

The drawing-room of the Marshall house. The day of the Bicycle Parade. **Peter** *and his father (***Josiah Marshall***) are sitting drinking tea after lunch, while* **Louise** *is pacing anxiously up and down.*

Louise Marshall   Well, may I or may I not?

Josiah Marshall   This time, as it is all arranged. But listen carefully, my girl. I give you liberty beyond what most folk would, but I'll not have you making a laughing stock of yourself or of me. I've a position to keep up. *(Pointing to a paper on a side-table)* This Suffragette rubbish is not entering my house. Votes for Women! That shameless hussy inciting women to go and break windows in the House of Commons and anywhere else they fancy. The ducking-stool is what she needs. Saying it in the Albert Hall, what's more!

Louise Marshall   If you mean Mrs Pankhurst's speech, then I'm with her all the way.

Peter Marshall   Fighting talk, Lou!

Josiah Marshall   I've let you join this, what you call it, Women's Suffrage Movement. They are fools, but at least they are respectable fools. A good many highly respected names. Solid financial backing.

Louise Marshall   You make it sound like the Stock Exchange.

Peter Marshall   Sailing close to the wind!

Both **Josiah** *and* **Louise** *turn on* **Peter.**

Josiah Marshall   I'll thank you to mind your own business, sir.

Louise Marshall   Stop interfering, Peter.

Peter Marshall   *(Getting up and moving to one side of the stage)* Your friends, Lou. Just coming up the drive. The tall one looks worried, but that dumpy one seems bold enough. She's a firecracker. What did you say her name was?

Louise Marshall   Emily Palmer.

Josiah Marshall	*(Standing up)* Well, I don't want to see them, you hear me? Take them straight to the stables where those infernal machines are. *(He takes out a gold half-hunter watch from his waistcoat pocket and clicks it open to check the time.)* Not even got the manners to arrive at a respectable time.
Louise Marshall	It is after half past two, Father.

*The door opens and a **maid** enters.*

Maid	Two ladies to see Miss Louise.
Louise Marshall	Well, don't leave my friends standing in the hall. Show them in and bring us a tray of tea.
Josiah Marshall	And how many more of these *friends* are we to expect?
Louise Marshall	Three. There's to be six altogether.
Peter Marshall	*(Pretending he is sword-fighting)* The Swashbuckling Six!
Louise Marshall	You can come about four-thirty. You know the route. And whatever you do, don't forget the hamper.
Josiah Marshall	A son of mine joining in these damn silly frolics. Where's your sense of pride gone?
Louise Marshall	Oh Father, we're only going for a bicycle ride and a picnic. *(Putting a hand on his arm and tweaking the end of his moustache)* Come on, Daddy, don't be cross!

> ***Josiah Marshall** crosses the stage, almost knocking over **Vera** and **Emily** who are just entering. The **maid** enters, sets down a tray of tea, passes round cups and then exits.*

Josiah Marshall	Twaddle, that's what it is, twaddle.

> ***Louise** pulls a face at her father as he exits.*

Louise Marshall   I'm so glad you've come after all. I was afraid you wouldn't. I know it's a long way. There are three more to come, Una and Maude Holiday and Mrs Jane Barrat. Do you know them?

Emily and Vera shake their heads.

Louise Marshall   There will be people enjoying Sunday leisure in the suburbs so they are bound to see a group of female cyclists. After all the important thing is to be noticed and have the placards read.

The maid enters to announce visitors.

Maid   The Misses Una and Maude Holiday.

Una and Maude Holiday appear.

Louise Marshall   Come in. Let me introduce you to two friends of mine. Una and Maude, this is Emily Palmer and Vera Bradshaw.

Una Holiday   I'm afraid Mrs Barrat is unable to be with us. Her eldest boy is ill again.

Louise Marshall   Again?

Una Holiday   He does suffer from asthma.

Louise Marshall   Perhaps. But I'm more inclined to think it is yet another example of cold feet. However there's nothing more to say. Let's check the placards.

She exits.

Peter Marshall   *(To Emily)* I've mended your bicycle. In fact when I'd finished the repairs I gave it a touch of paint. I think you'll find it as good as new.

Emily Palmer   Thanks. That's very good of yo.

Louise re-enters carrying a number of placards with VOTES FOR WOMEN clearly painted on them.

Louise Marshall   Pete, be a dear and fix these onto our bicycles for me.

Peter Marshall   What happened to your principles? I thought women were able to cope with anything just as well as, if not better than, mere men!

Louise Marshall   Of course they are, but we're all ready to set off.

Peter Marshall   Well, it's no use going without the placards.

Louise Marshall   Very well, don't help then. Give me some pliers and we'll do it! Come on, ladies, let's go!

> *The **women** exit, carrying the placards, leaving **Peter** standing centre-stage gazing after **Emily**.*

Scene Nine

The street outside Mrs Harris's Dress Shop. **Emily Palmer** *is coming out of the door on her way home, when* **Louise Marshall** *walks briskly by.*

Louise Marshall Oh, I'm so glad I caught you, before you left for home. I want some help. Can we talk for a moment?

Emily Palmer What is it? Tell me quick or Mam'll wonder what I've been doing.

Louise Marshall We've got to do something positive. More than just parading ourselves on bicycles. Make a stand. Show them we're not to be trifled with.

Emily Palmer Who?

Louise Marshall You are with me, aren't you? I mean, I can trust you?

Emily looks around nervously and moves Louise further away from the entrance of the shop.

Emily Palmer Of course yo can. But I don't understand.

Louise Marshall I've thought of a plan, but I can't do it alone. I'm sick to death of these useless meetings. You've been to some so you know what they're like — nothing but words. We need action if we're ever going to get the Vote. People take notice of action, especially drastic action.

Two of the girls, **Flo** *and* **Alice,** *come out of the shop and walk off-stage past* **Emily** *and* **Louise,** *saying goodnight as they go.*

Emily Palmer What sort of things was yo thinking of?

Louise Marshall We should take a leaf out of Mrs Pankhurst's book.

Emily Palmer Break windows yo mean?

Louise Marshall No. I had something else in mind.

Emily Palmer	What then?
Louise Marshall	Promise you won't let me down?

Emily nods.

Louise Marshall	It will have to be at night. That's the only time no one will be about. Your part is to get hold of some lengths of material, green, purple and white. Can you do that?
Emily Palmer	I don't know. There might be some scraps, but Mrs Harris is that mingy, she don't give much away.
Louise Marshall	Oh well, it doesn't matter. I'll buy some and give it to you. Probably the best thing in the long run. Less likely to be found out. It's the sewing I want you to do. I'm hopeless. We'll need eighteen flags altogether, striped with the three colours. How fast can you make them?
Emily Palmer	Depends how early we get let out. We sometimes have to work late when there's a rush job. It's busy now with Easter trade building up.
Louise Marshall	It's Wednesday today. Say Saturday night or Sunday?
Emily Palmer	Better say Sunday. But why? What are yo going to do?
Louise Marshall	It's what *we* are going to do, Emily. We're going to the golf course at Hardwick and we'll replace all the flags on the greens with the ones you make. Then we are going to paint VOTES FOR WOMEN in huge letters on the grass in whitewash. You won't let me down, will you?
Emily Palmer	*(Clearly stunned by the plan)* Of course not.

Peter Marshall enters from the other side of the stage.

Peter Marshall	Come on, Lou. I'm sure Miss Palmer doesn't want to stand listening to you in the street for ever!
Louise Marshall	I'll be with you in a minute, Pete. *(To* **Emily***)* See you next Sunday, then. Midnight, by the bottom of the golf course. *(She follows after* **Peter***)* And don't forget the flags!

Scene Ten

The kitchen in the Palmer household a few minutes later. **Mr Palmer** *is sitting in a chair.* **Mrs Palmer** *is working at the range.* **Emily** *enters.*

Mr Palmer   Shut the bloody door, can't yo? There's a draught like a cut-throat razor.

Emily Palmer   Sorry, Dad.

May Palmer enters.

May Palmer   Give us a hand, Emmie.

Emily helps May into a chair.

Emily Palmer   What's up? Mam's scowling fit for slaughter and Dad's scratchy.

May Palmer   Don't know. I went upstairs to get out of the way. Miss Barnes lent me a lovely story to read today. She says I can keep it as long as I like. But I have to give it back before I leave school at Easter.

Emily Palmer   Yo been reading by streetlight again? Yo'll hurt your eyes.

Ernie enters noisily.

Ernie Palmer   I'll need a clean shirt for tonight, Mam. There's a special meeting been called up at the Chapel. I'm speaking.

Mrs Palmer   Well I'm not bloody ironing it! As if I've not enough on my plate, cooking and cleaning for the lot of yo.

Ernie Palmer   Our Emmie can do it.

Emily Palmer   I've other chores.

Mrs Palmer   Yo do it, girl, when yo're asked.

Emily Palmer   Why should I?

Mrs Palmer   Because I'm telling yo, that's why. And if yo don't like it yo know what yo can do.

Emily Palmer	But that's not fair. Why should Ernie just sit there while I iron *his* shirt?
Mr Palmer	Can't yo two shut up? Yammering like a pair of alley cats. Where's my supper? I've been out breaking my back all day and come home to a lot of screeching women.

Emily stomps off stage and slams the door.

• •

Scene Eleven

The golf-course, on the edge of a green, just after midnight. The first part of the scene is played at the front of the stage, where a policeman is standing. **Emily** *enters.*

Constable	Cold night to be out, Miss. Late too.
Emily Palmer	Sharp frost, too. I'll be glad to get home.
Constable	Goodnight, Miss.
Emily Palmer	Goodnight.

*Emily walks stealthily onto the stage and waits in the shadows, where **Louise** has been waiting, hidden.*

Louise Marshall	I thought you'd never get here. You're late!
Emily Palmer	I'm sorry, I couldn't leave before everyone was asleep.
Louise Marshall	It doesn't matter. Have you got the flags?
Emily Palmer	Yes.
Louise Marshall	I've got scissors and brushes. The can of whitewash is under that bush. Let's make a start.
Emily Palmer	Why is it so important to you?
Louise Marshall	Isn't it important to you?

Emily Palmer   Yes, but . . .

Louise Marshall   I met someone. Mary Grant. She came up from London to speak at one of our meetings. It was incredible listening to her. She has been in Holloway Prison four times and she described the way she was forcibly fed. Oh, it's monstrous! It's disgusting! She was so frail, yet she had the courage of a lion. Those prison doctors are brutes. Some of the things she said made me want to vomit.

Emily Palmer   Would yo do it? Go on hunger strike, I mean?

Louise Marshall   I believe I could. Thinking about it now, in the open air. But it's when you're there, shut away inside prison that counts.

Emily Palmer   Are yo going to keep on doing things like tonight?

Louise Marshall   This is just the beginning. You'll see. Here, cut off the old flag and tie on one of ours. I'll start painting.

Emily Palmer   What made yo pick on a golf-course?

Louise Marshall   Private property. Owned by wealthy men, like my father. They don't like their property damaged. It's sacred.

Emily Palmer   Your father will be furious.

Louise Marshall   Serves him right. I'm not his property. Just think of the newspaper headlines this little lot will cause.

> *Emily* looks horrified as if she has not fully realised the effects of what she is doing.

Louise Marshall   We have to cross the farm track to the other part of the course now.

> *Sound of a dog barking off-stage.*

Louise Marshall   It's all right, he's tied up.

Emily Palmer   But we ain't finished yet.

Keeper   *(Off-stage)* All right, Tiger, down boy.

Louise Marshall	The dog's free. Run!
	*Emily turns to run away. **Louise** turns and twists her ankle, falling heavily to the ground.*
Louise Marshall	Go, can't you!
	*Emily bends down to help **Louise**. The keeper enters carrying a double-barrelled shot gun, which he points at the women.*
Keeper	Right you two, don't try anything or I'll pepper you good and proper. *(Seeing who they are)* Well, I'll be danged. A couple of gels! You'd better come with me.
	He escorts them off stage.

• •

Scene Twelve

	*The kitchen of the Palmer house. Two weeks later. **Emily** is ironing. There is a knock at the door and **Vera Bradshaw** enters.*
Vera Bradshaw	*(Rushing over to hug Emily)* You was splendid in court, Emmie. Mad but splendid. I'd have come round the same night only I felt bad and went back to me lodgings and bed. Been there ever since. *(She coughs violently.)*
Emily Palmer	Here, come in and sit down. Yo sound as if yo didn't ought to have got up.
Vera Bradshaw	Oh, I'm all right. I've got news for you. I've left Ma Harris's. Got a job in London. Look, I've had this letter from Mrs Silver. I used to know her before. She came to the house where I was in service, to do plain sewing. She's set up in business now for herself, got premises in Soho. She's done that well she needs help, so she's wrote and asked me.
Emily Palmer	I'm ever so pleased for yo.

Vera Bradshaw	There's something else an' all. Mrs Silver wants two girls. Asked me if I knew anyone. Well, ever since the court-case and Ma Harris giving you your notice, I've been that worried so of course I thought of you. *(Vera starts a coughing fit.)*
Emily Palmer	Come by the fire. There's a pot of tea on the hob. Yo have a drink and get your breath. I was just getting some tea for May. She'll be back from school in a jiffy. I never knew yo had worked in London.
Vera Bradshaw	Lived near Hyde Park. A tall house with iron railings around it in one of them London squares.
Emily Palmer	Sounds very grand.
Vera Bradshaw	It was right enough.
Emily Palmer	Tweeny* were yo?
Vera Bradshaw	Parlourmaid. I would have been a cook, that's what I intended.
Emily Palmer	What happened?

> *Vera shrugs her shoulders and obviously doesn't want to answer. Enter* **Mrs Palmer**.

Mrs Palmer	Yo're off work early, Vera. My word it's cold. There'll be some sleet before long. It's a good thing there ain't such a load today.
Emily Palmer	Mam's found herself a little job. Washes for three or four folks round the Vicarage. I help with a bit of ironing. *(She pours tea for* **Vera** *and her mother)* Take the weight off your feet, Mam, I've got a surprise for yo.
Mrs Palmer	What's that then? *(**Mrs Palmer** pulls off her shoes and sits by the range.)*
Emily Palmer	I've got an offer of a job.
Mrs Palmer	Doing what?

---

* A tweeny was the 'between maid' who helped both the cook and the housemaid.

Emily Palmer	To go to London with Vera and work for a lady that runs a dressmaking business there.
Mrs Palmer	That's a long way off!

*Enter **May**, her limp more pronounced after her walk from school.*

May Palmer	What's a long way off?
Emily Palmer	London. I'm going to work there.
May Palmer	Oh Emmie, yo ain't? *(She bursts into tears.)*
Emily Palmer	Don't cry, my lovie. We won't be parted forever. I'll be back to see yo. Or yo can come for a visit.
Mrs Palmer	Give over, May. Here, sit down and get your tea. A bit of food inside yo'll put a different face on things. Our Emmie can't hang around this house forever without work.

Vic Palmer enters.

Vic Palmer	What's this then, somebody died?
Mrs Palmer	Our Emmie's off to London.
Vic Palmer	That right?
Emily Palmer	Yes.
Vic Palmer	When will yo be off?
Vera Bradshaw	Soon as we can. In a few days I should think. After I've sent a message to let Mrs Silver know we're coming.

There is a loud knock at the front door, off-stage.

Emily Palmer	I'll go.

Emily walks to the front of the stage where we imagine the door to be. **Peter Marshall** *enters. Both are clearly embarrassed to see each other.*

Emily Palmer   Please won't yo come in?

While **Peter** *and* **Emily** *talk, those in the kitchen area 'freeze' so as not to distract the audience from their conversation.*

Peter Marshall   *(Handing* **Emily** *a lilac envelope)* Lou asked me to bring this. Just a note to say thank you. 'Fraid it's the first opportunity I've had. Since the, er, golf-course business Father has been keeping a tight rein. Lou is confined to the house and I am being pressed to join the delights of business management.

Emily Palmer   I'm that grateful to yo for getting me out of that mess over my fine. I can't pay yo back at present. Things have been a bit tight. Money I mean. But when I start my new job in London I'll send the money regular. Yo won't mind if it's in small amounts? I don't suppose I shall be able to manage more than two and a tanner a week.

Peter Marshall   Don't think about the fine. Regard it as my contribution to Women's Rights.

Emily Palmer   But I can't accept . . .

Peter Marshall   Rubbish. I don't want to hear another word on the subject.

Emily Palmer   But won't your father be angry?

Peter Marshall   *(Laughing)* I don't tell him about things like that. What was that about going to London?

Emily Palmer   Vera Bradshaw and me. We've been offered places working for a dressmaker she knows in Soho. That's part of London.

Peter Marshall   *(Trying not to smile at this)* When do you start?

Emily Palmer   I don't know yet. Why?

Peter Marshall	I was just thinking. I ought to explain that Louise and I are travelling up to London next week. Father wants us to spend Easter with Aunt Gertrude and Uncle Henry. He thinks we won't be able to get up to any mischief there. I was going to suggest giving you a seat in the car. Miss Bradshaw, too, if she wishes. There's plenty of room for four and all the luggage . . . Well?
Emily Palmer	Er . . . just a minute.

*She fetches **Vera** from the kitchen area of the stage. They whisper to each other briefly.*

Peter Marshall	Well, what do you say?
Emily Palmer	Thanks ever so. We'd love to say yes.
Peter Marshall	I am glad. We'll call round on Wednesday, then, nice and early. Say half past nine.
Emily Palmer	Oh no!
Peter Marshall	What's wrong?
Emily Palmer	I, er, we'd better meet you somewhere else. Down by the corner of Summer Hill Terrace and Sandpits. Easier for Vera. She won't have to carry her bag so far.
Peter Marshall	Au revoir. I'll tell Lou. Don't crumple the letter before you've read it!

Act Two

Scene One

*Mrs Silver's sitting room. To one side is a hatstand. Centre-stage is a tailor's dummy draped with material. **Mrs Silver** is pinning up the material. On the other side **Vera** sits, sewing, at a table. Enter **Emily** wearing a coat and hat. She carries a bundle.*

Mrs Silver   Oh there you are, Emily. What took you so long, my dear? Did you get everything?

Emily Palmer   *(Taking off coat and hat and hanging them on the hatstand)* Everything except the cording. Mr Bootley says he can order, so I told him to do that. It'll take five days though. *(She hands the bundle to Mrs Silver.)*

Mrs Silver   *(Straightening up from the tailor's dummy to take the bundle)* This wretched lumbago's plaguing me today. I'll have to take a dose and see if I can't shift it.

She exits, carrying the bundle.

Emily sits down and begins sewing.

Emily Palmer   I got a news-sheet. Mrs Pankhurst's been released from Holloway again. They'll surely not re-arrest her after the trouble last time.

Vera Bradshaw	Course they will. Wicked, letting her out just to get well after starving, only to whisk her back. Cat and Mouse is just the right nickname for that . . . law! *(She coughs.)*
Emily Palmer	Yo all right? Yo look a bit flushed.
Vera Bradshaw	Good enough. There's a letter for you. *(She pushes a letter across the table to **Emily**.)*

*Emily opens a letter and reads it to herself. Enter **Mrs Silver**.*

Mrs Silver	I've popped the kettle on while I was up there. Nothing to beat a good strong cup of tea. Better than all your medicine. Not bad news I hope, Emily?
Emily Palmer	It's from my sister, May. Things aren't good back home. Dad's out of work.
Vera Bradshaw	Oh no!
Emily Palmer	Vic's out on strike. He sends yo his respects, Vera. *(**Vera** looks down on her sewing, embarrassed.)* Mam's going to have another baby. And if that isn't bad enough, Mrs Harris says she won't have no more Palmers and May can't find work nowhere else. She wants to come and work for yo, Mrs Silver.
Mrs Silver	For me?
Emily Palmer	She's a dab hand with a needle, and willing.
Mrs Silver	Well, I don't know.
Emily Palmer	I'd look after her, just board and keep that's all. She could have part of my wages for her own bits.
Mrs Silver	I suppose I could do with more help. How old is she?
Emily Palmer	Twelve last March.
Mrs Silver	Twelve! I thought . . . no matter. I'll take her anyway. There's a lot to be said for training someone in your own methods. Tell her to get here as soon as she can.

*Emily takes **Mrs Silver**'s hand in both of hers and kisses it.*

Emily Palmer   Oh thank you, Mrs Silver. Thank you.

Mrs Silver   Well, I never did!

· ·

Scene Two

*Mrs Boston's sitting room. **Louise Marshall** and **Mary Grant** are sitting on a sofa. On a small table there is an extravagant hat. Enter **Emily** carrying a box.*

Louise Marshall   *(Standing up)* Emily Palmer! Where have you been all these weeks?

Emily Palmer   *(Stammering)* I . . . I've brought your aunt's dress . . . and I'm . . . sorry not to have seen yo, but we've been that busy.

Louise Marshall   *(Taking the box and putting it to one side)* Come on. I want to introduce you. Emily, this is Mary Grant. Mary . . . Emily Palmer, a very good friend and sympathizer.

Emily and Louise sit down.

Mary Grant   It's always good to meet another comrade. I've heard of your exploit in Birmingham.

Emily Palmer   I'd do it again, given the chance.

Louise Marshall   You mean that?

Emily Palmer   Yes.

Louise Marshall	Tell her, Mary.
Mary Grant	We're planning a continuous speech at a Liberal Party meeting. The idea is that everyone chosen to take part learns the speech by heart and one by one we stand up in the audience and interrupt the proceedings. We're bound to be thrown out, of course, but as one goes, there will always be another one to carry on.
Louise Marshall	You could do it, Emily. I'm sure you could. I'm going to start the ball rolling.
Emily Palmer	Me . . . speak?
Louise Marshall	Mary's got it all written out and had copies made. You can even read it if you aren't too good at remembering. Do say you will.
Emily Palmer	But if we're caught we're bound to be arrested. And Mrs Silver will turn me out for sure.
Mary Grant	Well, if you're worried about your job, of course . . .
Emily Palmer	No, I'll do it.
Louise Marshall	Splendid!
Mary Grant	Here's the speech. *(She takes some sheets of paper out of her bag and hands them to* **Emily***.)* I'll give you two and if you can interest anyone else, please do so. They can always speak up at the end if we exhaust our planned eight speakers. Don't forget, you will be number three in order. Now I must go. *(She stands up and takes* **Emily's** *hand.)* I'm so glad we have met. Caxton Hall, a week next Thursday, eight-thirty.
Louise Marshall	I'll show you out.
	Mary and Louise exit. Emily walks restlessly around the room, picks up the hat and stands facing the audience, trying it on as if standing before a mirror. Enter Peter, behind her.
Peter Marshall	How nice you look.

Embarrassed, **Emily** *reaches up to take the hat off.*

Peter Marshall   No, don't take it off. It suits you.

She stands there for a moment with the hat still on while **Peter** *looks at her admiringly.*

Emily Palmer   I really must be getting back.

Peter Marshall   Oh, won't you stay for a while? It's such a long time since I saw you. Of course Louise gives me odd bits of news now and again, but it's not the same as live conversation. I want to know how you are liking your job. Is it a good place? And has Louise inveigled you into any more Suffragette schemes?

Emily Palmer   The job's all right. Are yo on a visit?

Peter Marshall   Shall we say I'm a long-term guest, until I get a place of my own. I'm in charge of Father's London office. Quite a reformed character. Between ourselves it's a good deal more convenient for getting out to Hurlingham. I'm shortly to qualify as a fully trained balloon pilot. I know, why don't you come for a flight sometime?

Emily Palmer   Oh . . . I'm not sure.

Peter Marshall   Do say yes. It would be a splendid lark.

Emily makes no reply. Peter moves closer to her.

Peter Marshall   That hat. You look stunning. A regular Gibson Girl.*

Emily Palmer   Yo needs specs if that's what yo thinks.

Peter reaches forward and tilts her head upwards to look her in the eyes.

---

* A Gibson Girl was a fashionable girl of the type drawn by the American artist, C. Dana Gibson, in the early 1890s.

A 'Gibson Girl'

Peter Marshall	You don't believe me, do you?

> *Peter kisses her clumsily on the cheek. She steps back. There is an awkward silence between them. Emily takes off the hat.*

Peter Marshall	I beg your pardon. I didn't think you'd mind.

> *Enter Louise.*

Louise Marshall	Hello, Pete. Didn't know you were back. Uncle Henry's just come in. He said if I saw you to say he wants a word.
Peter Marshall	I'd better go and beard the lion in his den. Goodbye for the present.

> *Exit Peter.*

Louise Marshall	Sit down then. You look so uncomfortable standing in the middle of the room.

> *Emily and Louise sit down.*

Louise Marshall	You're very quiet. Has Peter been upsetting you?
Emily Palmer	Oh no, of course not.
Louise Marshall	That's good. Now then, let's talk about our plans.

• •

Scene Three

> *The foyer of Caxton Hall. Emily and Vic are standing waiting. Enter Louise and Mary.*

Louise Marshall	Hello, Emily.
Emily Palmer	I'm that glad to see yo. I was beginning to think yo'd been prevented from coming after all. This is my brother, Vic. Vic – Miss Louise Marshall, Miss Mary Grant.

Vic Palmer	Pleased to meet yo both.
Emily Palmer	He's come down on the train with my sister, May. He knows about our plans.
Mary Grant	And he approves?
Vic Palmer	Yo women have a raw deal. There's too much injustice in this world. I reckon it's time someone made a stand.

Enter Vera.

Vic Palmer	Hello again, Vera.
Vera Bradshaw	Hello, Vic.
Mary Grant	I think we'd better go in now that everybody's here. The others have already taken their places. Remember to spread out.

> *Vera, Emily, Vic, Louise and Mary descend from the stage and take up seats that have been left vacant in the audience. Enter the Chairman. As he is speaking, Louise gets to her feet and unrolls a green, white and purple banner with VOTES FOR WOMEN written on it.*

Chairman   Ladies and gentlemen, I'd like to begin by thanking you all for coming here tonight. It is most gratifying to see such a splendid turn-out and I feel I am justified in seeing it as a vote of confidence in the policies and practice of the Liberal party. As you know, our principal speaker is the Right Honourable Reginald McKenna, who needs no further introduction from me.

> *The cry of 'Suffragettes' comes from different parts of the hall, followed by 'Shame!' and 'Throw her out!'*

Louise Marshall   Ladies and gentlemen, it is an outrage that this meeting should be taking place while women up and down the country are prevented from expressing deeply-held beliefs and refused the opportunity to participate fully in the life of this nation. Our country stands accused as the world looks on. It is the shame of England that half its population should be treated thus, denied the privilege as are convicts and . . .

Louise is dragged from the hall.

Mary Grant . . . convicts and lunatics. Is this the mark of a mature and well-tried civilization, or will in years to come the finger of scorn and derision be pointed at . . .

Mary is dragged from the hall.

Emily Palmer . . . be pointed at Mr Asquith and his so-called Liberal government. Yo may think their 'rule democratic, but future generations will pronounce it a tyranny, a dictatorship, a monstrous travesty of justice. My friends yo cannot sit here unmoved. We ask yo all . . .

Emily can clearly be seen throwing punches at those who are attempting to move her. Stage lights are blacked out. Confused cries.

•••

Scene Four

*Mrs Silver's sitting room. **Mrs Silver** is sitting, sewing. Enter **Emily**, panting, dishevelled and with a bruise showing around her eye.*

Mrs Silver Emily! My Gawd! Whatever happened?

Emily shakes her head and sobs.

Mrs Silver Here, you sit yourself down.

She exits and returns with a bottle of brandy and a glass. She pours out some brandy.

Mrs Silver Drink this. It's just a drop of brandy.

Emily drinks.

Mrs Silver Now then. Tell me all about it.

Emily Palmer	I might as well. Yo'll most likely find out anyway. I've been to Caxton Hall.
Mrs Silver	What, to hear the politicians speak?
Emily Palmer	No, to make a protest.
Mrs Silver	What sort of protest?
Emily Palmer	To speak up for the right to vote.
Mrs Silver	On your own?
Emily Palmer	No, there was eight of us. Me and Vera and Miss Marshall (Mrs Boston's niece) and some others. Things got pretty rough. Vic was right in the middle of it . . . and Vera. I had to fight to get away. One of them gave me this. *(Points to her eye)*
Mrs Silver	The devils!
Emily Palmer	*(Surprised)* Yo ain't mad then?
Mrs Silver	Not at you, I'm not. But at those bigots sitting up there in the House of Commons with their fat stomachs and self-important airs. We'd better bathe that eye of yours.
Emily Palmer	It's all right.
Mrs Silver	You don't know what became of Vera, then?
Emily Palmer	No, nor of Vic. They must have been arrested.
Mrs Silver	Well it's too late to do much tonight. I'll go round the police station in the morning. If there's bail to be had or fines to pay, you needn't worry, my dear. Put it down to my contribution to the Cause.

Scene Five

*Mary Grant's flat. **Mary, Louise** and **Emily** are sitting, talking. There is a tray on a table before them with tea-cups, a teapot and a plate of cakes.*

Mary Grant	I'm so pleased you made time to visit us. We've been talking about you a lot since Louise came out of prison this time. There's a scheme afoot . . . just up your street . . . but I'm putting the cart before the horse. Tea first, before it gets cold. Are you comfortable, Louise?
Louise Marshall	I'll be easier when my bones are padded a little. I lost nine pounds last stretch, and I wasn't bonny when I went in.
Emily Palmer	It's vile! I don't know how yo stands it, chased around all the time. Detectives after yo, ready to pounce as soon as yo shows your face on a platform.
Louise Marshall	Adds spice, you know. Why I'm quite a celebrity these days. Detective Inspector Mason is specially assigned to hunt me down.
Mary Grant	Now don't bother about that. You are safe enough in my flat. All you have to do for the present is get back your strength. Here, eat one of these lovely stodgy buns, guaranteed to put weight on the skinniest.
Emily Palmer	But it's a crime! They hunt us like wild animals when it's them that are the beasts.
Mary Grant	There's been some talk at Headquarters of forming a bodyguard to protect Mrs Pankhurst and the other leaders.
Louise Marshall	You'd be good at that, Emily.
Mary Grant	The women picked have to be brave enough and have the physique to take punishment.
Emily Palmer	Are yo are asking me?
Mary Grant	The way you acquitted yourself at Caxton Hall didn't go unnoticed.

Emily Palmer	If yo thinks I can do it, I'm willing. Anything's better than sitting on your backside all day long. I ain't done nothing more daring since Caxton Hall than throw a bit of chalk at a doctor's window in Harley Street. It didn't even break the glass.
Mary Grant	Then that's agreed. If you come to Lincoln's Inn House next week you can learn all the details.

● ●

Scene Six

Night. Outside Mrs Silver's house. **Peter** *is standing, waiting. Enter* **Emily.**

Peter Marshall	Emily.
Emily Palmer	What are you doing here?
Peter Marshall	I've been waiting a long time.
Emily Palmer	For me?
Peter Marshall	Vera said you were out. I calculated it wouldn't be for the whole night. She wasn't very forthcoming about when you'd be back.
Emily Palmer	I couldn't come straight back. I was followed.
Peter Marshall	Followed? By whom?
Emily Palmer	Detectives, of course. They were waiting outside the hall where we were training. They took photographs of everyone who came out.
Peter Marshall	How did you get away then?
Emily Palmer	A constable came down the other side of the road. I ran to him and said, "Oh please, sir, can yo help me ? That man is following me." And while the two of them were busy getting acquainted I ran away as fast as I could. *(She laughs)* But I didn't expect to find yo waiting on the doorstep.
Peter Marshall	I want to know where Louise is living.

Emily Palmer	Don't yo know?
Peter Marshall	I'd hardly be asking you if I did.
Emily Palmer	If she don't choose to tell yo, then it's not for me to say.
Peter Marshall	But that's ridiculous.
Emily Palmer	No it ain't. It's common sense.
Peter Marshall	Come on, I have to know. It's important.
Emily Palmer	It's important she gets rest and quiet to build up her strength. One careless word and she'd be back inside before yo could say knife, and I ain't going to betray her.
Peter Marshall	It's not a question of betrayal. I'd not ask you if it wasn't urgent. I'd never try and make you betray a trust. But you are my only hope. Lou hasn't written since the Caxton Hall affair when Father told her not to come back home. I tried to smooth things over, visited her in prison and offered to pay her fine, but she's as pig-headed as he is. Two of a kind! And now Father's had a stroke. He can't speak. If he could he'd no doubt refuse to go back on his word, but I know in his heart he wants to see her before he dies.
Emily Palmer	He ain't going to get better?

Peter shakes his head.

Emily Palmer	Yo know she's on the Cat and Mouse rack★?
Peter Marshall	I didn't know.
Emily Palmer	She's out of prison, like I said, but they want her back. If I tell yo, the police might find out where she is.

★ Cat and Mouse rack: in 1913 what became known as the 'Cat and Mouse Act' was introduced to respond to the force-feeding of suffragettes. Women who became ill through prison hunger strikes were released and then taken back into prison if they were involved in further activity – like a cat playing with a mouse.

| Peter Marshall | So that's what you think of me? |

Peter takes her hand.

| Peter Marshall | You will tell me? |
| Emily Palmer | Yes, all right. |

Peter kisses her hand.

Emily Palmer	I'd better take yo, so as there won't be no misunderstandings. But not tonight. In the morning. It's time I went in.
Peter Marshall	I'll call round tomorrow then. What time?
Emily Palmer	Make it eleven. We shan't be noticed at that time of day. Goodnight.
Peter Marshall	Goodbye, Emily. And thank you.

. . . .

Scene Seven

*Mrs Silver's sitting room. **Emily** is sitting restlessly. **Mrs Silver** is sewing.*

Mrs Silver	No good clock-watching, my dear. Best way to make time go slowly. Besides we don't know when she will get here. The note just said Thursday. No mention of the time.
Emily Palmer	Only three hours to go. We'll never get to the Hippodrome in time.
Mrs Silver	If she says she will be here, then she will be here. Though how she'll escape detection, I can't imagine.
Emily Palmer	She's still on the wanted list. Supposing she's caught.
Mrs Silver	That's someone at the door now. You just wait here.

*Exit **Mrs Silver**. She returns with **Louise**, dressed in black.*

Louise Marshall	Lady Grandison to see Mrs Silver and Miss Palmer. How do you do? *(She laughs.)*
Emily Palmer	Louise, I hardly recognise yo! All that black crepe. Yo look like a widow.
Louise Marshall	An orphan.
Emily Palmer	Oh, I'm sorry. I wasn't thinking.
Louise Marshall	It doesn't matter. Father died two weeks ago. So now there is nothing to prevent me getting back to work.
Emily Palmer	Tell us how yo got here safe.
Louise Marshall	Pete and I travelled by car as male companions till just outside London. Then we stopped and I changed into all this stuff. When we reached Aunt Gertrude's, Pete bundled me into a cab. And here I am.
Mrs Silver	And here are your costumes. *(She holds up two colourful dresses)* This is yours, Louise. And here's Emily's.
Louise Marshall	Oh, Emily! You'll look like a bird of paradise in this.
Emily Palmer	Jackdaw more like, or a magpie. Talk about ridiculous! Beauty and the Beast, that's what we'll be, only the beast was a man and I'm not.
Louise Marshall	Oh nonsense! You've got a bee in your bonnet about your looks.
Emily Palmer	A side of beef with hair on top. Untidy at that.
Louise Marshall	I believe you mean it.
Emily Palmer	Well, I've got eyes.
Louise Marshall	With the blinds drawn. Pete says you remind him of the country; haymaking and jars of cider and bees buzzing round cornfield poppies.
Emily Palmer	A regular peasant.

Mrs Silver	Come on, you two, we haven't got all day you know. Let's get you both made up. We'll start with you, Emily. Sit down.

Mrs Silver begins making up Emily's face.

Mrs Silver	What are you going to call your act then?
Louise Marshall	It's all arranged. Haven't you seen the programme? 'Emmie and Lou, Plenty of Patter, with Songs at the Piano.'
Emily Palmer	*(Laughs)* Looks as if I'm left with the songs then.
Louise Marshall	I've heard you speak out, Emily Palmer. Remember Caxton Hall.
Emily Palmer	Do yo think the police will have found out it's really a WSPU meeting?
Louise Marshall	I expect so. They have spies everywhere.
Emily Palmer	We might not even get in.
Louise Marshall	We'll get in. Don't you worry. I just hope they don't break it up before we have a proper chance to speak.
Emily Palmer	*(Taking out her Indian club*)* Just let them try it. I'll be ready.

---

* An Indian Club was a weighted club used in gymnastic exercises.

Scene Eight

*A large cell in the police station. A number of women, including **Emily**, are crouched on the floor. One of them is crying quietly. Enter a **policeman**, leading **Vera**. He thrusts her roughly forward.*

Emily Palmer   Vera?

Vera Bradshaw   Emmie! Oh, Emmie, I'm so pleased it's you.

Emily Palmer   But I didn't know you were coming to the meeting. Yo never said.

Vera Bradshaw   I came on the spur of the moment. I'd been thinking – a long time. I'm a coward, Emmie. That's the long and the short of it. You don't know how I admire all of you who make a stand for your beliefs. But being afraid . . . it's like a maggot eating your insides. In the end I couldn't bear it and when Mrs Silver said, 'Go on, have the time off, I'd go myself if my back would let me,' I made up my mind I'd be like you and Miss Marshall. I'd not run away. *(She collapses into a coughing fit.)*

Emily Palmer   Yo don't know how good it is to know someone else is as scared as me.

Vera Bradshaw   You . . . scared too?

Emily Palmer   Ready to wet myself with fright.

Vera Bradshaw   Emmie Palmer! Really!

Emily Palmer   *(Laughs)* Vera, yo're so proper, even down here.

*Vera laughs as well. Enter **policeman**.*

Policeman   Emily Palmer.

Emily Palmer   *(Standing up)* That's me.

Policeman   Come on.

Vera Bradshaw   Where are you taking her?

Policeman   Where d'you think? Up before the magistrate.

. . . .

Scene Nine

A cell in Holloway Prison. The cell has a small barred window. There is a bed, and a slop pail. On a small corner shelf are a bar of yellow soap, comb, tin mug, watercan and wash basin. **Emily** *is scrubbing the floor. The cell door opens and the* **wardress** *enters.*

Wardress   Not finished yet, thirteen?

>   *Emily* *slowly raises herself to her feet,*
>   *clutching at the corner shelf for support.*

Wardress   Supper not touched or cleared away? Slovenly habits, thirteen.
                    You'd best look sharp about it or you'll get no gruel. *(Seeing*
                    that this is producing no effect on the prisoner) Stubborn, eh?
                    You'll do yourself no good. Eat a morsel or you know what'll
                    happen. I can't stay here all day. If you insist on this foolishness,
                    you know what you'll get.

>   *She exits, slamming the door and locking*
>   *it.*

>   *Emily* *slumps to the floor, then looks*
>   *longingly at her tin mug which is full of*
>   *cocoa. She stretches out towards it as if she*
>   *is going to drink it, but, at the last*
>   *moment, hurls the contents onto the floor.*
>   *She then lies, face down, on her bed. A*
>   *doctor* *enters the cell, followed by two*
>   *wardresses.*

Doctor   Listen carefully to what I have to say. Food has been brought for
                    you and I give you a last chance to take it of your own free will.

>   *A* *wardress* *offers her a glass of water and*
>   *a bowl of gruel. Emily* *turns away from it.*

Doctor   Very well. I have no other course than to compel you to take
                    food.

>   *The* *wardresses* *strip off the bedding, pull*
>   *Emily* *roughly to her feet and put her on*
>   *a chair that one of them has brought in.*

Open your eyes, thirteen. *(The* *doctor* *is holding a long rubber*
tube.) You still have a choice. This must pass into your stomach.
It is easier by mouth.

>   *Emily* *clearly isn't going to cooperate.*

Doctor   Very well.

*The **doctor** signals to the **wardresses** who hold **Emily**'s shoulders and legs. She screams. The **doctor** forces the tube down into her stomach and starts to pour liquid into a funnel. Just as it appears they have managed to force feed her, her body heaves and she sprays them all with vomit.*

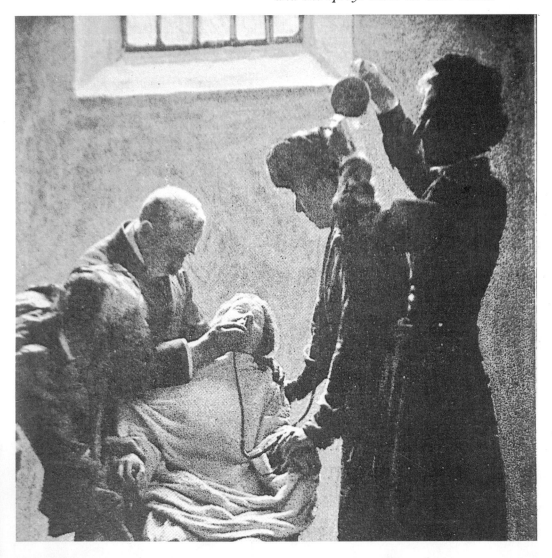

Scene Ten

Mrs Silver's sitting room. **Louise**, **Peter**, *and* **May** *are standing, waiting. Enter* **Mrs Silver** *with* **Emily** *leaning on her arm.*

Mrs Silver   Here she is.

A burst of applause from the others.

Emily Palmer   I'm ever so grateful.

Peter Marshall It's us who ought to be grateful for the privilege of being able to help, even in a small way.

Emily Palmer   Yo mean that?

Peter Marshall Of course.

Emily Palmer   But I thought you thought us loonies.

Peter Marshall I do. Stark raving mad, the lot of you. The world keeps producing such crazy fools, and often they do a lot of good.

Louise Marshall Welcome back to civilization. *(She kisses Emily.)*

May Palmer   *(Hugging Emily)* Oh Emmie, I thought yo was never going to get out. It seemed like ten thousand years. But it doesn't matter now yo're here. I've had a letter from Mam. The new baby's called Edith Emmeline. What do yo think of that? And Dad's back at work with Mr Treedle delivering beer barrels. He's boss of the dray and the horse is called Sweetheart.

Peter Marshall Hold hard. You'll leave no news for the rest of us.

Louise Marshall Here's something for you, Emily.

She hands **Emily** *a brown paper parcel.* **Emily** *opens it to reveal a purse.*

Louise Marshall Go on. Open it.

Emily opens the purse and takes out a brooch.

Emily Palmer	*(Reading aloud)* To Emily Palmer with grateful thanks for your courage and devotion, Emmeline Pankhurst.
May Palmer	I made the purse.
Peter Marshall	Speech!

The cry of 'Speech!' is taken up by the others.

Emily Palmer	Speeches ain't my line. Thanks ever so much. Yo don't know what a fraud I am. I don't deserve any of this. But I'll do better next time, see if I don't.

Applause from the others.

Emily Palmer	Where's Vera?

Silence from the others.

Emily Palmer	Where is she?
Louise Marshall	Sit down, Emily. There's something you should know.

● ●

Scene Eleven

Mrs Silver's sitting room. **Mary Grant** *and* **Emily** *are talking.*

Mary Grant	Will you come then, Emily?
Emily Palmer	I don't know.
Mary Grant	But a deputation to the King! It's bound to bring results.
Emily Palmer	If yo say so.
Mary Grant	Are you afraid?
Emily Palmer	No, of course not. I'm just not convinced any more.

Mary Grant	You aren't trying to tell me that you no longer care whether we achieve the right to vote? A person of your intelligence can't possibly . . .
Emily Palmer	No, it isn't that. It's just . . . all the violence. Where's it getting us?
Mary Grant	Nearer our goal.
Emily Palmer	With folk turning against us because of it and people dying for nothing. I've heard some of them say we deserve to die — 'Let 'em get on with it' — when we starve in prison.
Mary Grant	If you are thinking of Vera —
Emily Palmer	Course I'm thinking of her. I think of her all the time. It's such a waste. She'd only got one life. We all have. And to throw it away . . .
Mary Grant	Vera gave her life willingly, for the Cause. Just as I would, or Louise, or any of us if it had to be that way.
Emily Palmer	Did she?
Mary Grant	I won't press you, Emily. Everyone has to follow the dictates of their conscience. I'm disappointed, naturally, especially as Louise is in prison. I'd thought you would like to step in for her.

She turns to leave.

Emily Palmer	Wait . . . I'll come.
Mary Grant	Are you sure?
Emily Palmer	Yes.
Mary Grant	I'm glad. Now I'd better tell you the arrangements. It's planned for the twenty-first of May. We've organized a house in Grosvenor Place. It's at the back of Buckingham Palace, overlooking the gardens. Of course we shall have to be very careful not to make the police suspicious so the idea is to arrive in ones and twos over a period of days. It'll be a question of camping out I'm afraid.

Emily Palmer	That won't worry me. I've slept on the floor when my bed's been in hock* before now!
Mary Grant	Then, on the day, we will set out to walk up Constitution Hill to the gates of the Palace and try to gain entrance to deliver the Petition. After all, it is the right of every English man and woman to take their grievances to their King. In all fairness he must listen. And if there is any justice at all, he must surely come down on our side.
Emily Palmer	Of course he must. But is there any, Mary? Is there any justice at all?

. . . .

Scene Twelve

*Emily's bedroom. **Emily** is in bed. On a bedside table are some flowers and a bowl of fruit. **Dr Curtis** is standing over her. **Louise** is sitting beside her.*

Dr Curtis	She's come to.

Emily tries to sit up.

Emily Palmer	What's wrong with me?
Dr Curtis	Nothing that a bit of rest and care won't cure. You had a nasty knock on the head.
Louise Marshall	A horse kicked you, by the Wellington Gates, when you were with the Deputation. Peter brought you home. Don't you remember?
Dr Curtis	It'll all come back to her, in good time. I'll leave her in your hands, Miss Marshall. She's not to have too much disturbance, mind.

He exits.

---

* 'In hock' is the same as 'in pawn'. A pawn broker takes in goods in return for lending money and returns them when the debt (plus a fee) is paid.

Louise Marshall	Peter will be glad to hear you're all right. Look, he brought the flowers.
Emily Palmer	Louise.
Louise Marshall	Yes.
Emily Palmer	I've had such dreams.
Louise Marshall	Ssh! They're all over now.
Emily Palmer	There's something I've got to say.
Louise Marshall	The doctor says you need rest.
Emily Palmer	I've betrayed yo all. I've let yo down.
Louise Marshall	Don't be silly, Emily. The police broke up the Deputation. You did the best you could. Mrs Pankhurst got through. She delivered the letter to the King.
Emily Palmer	It ain't that. It's what I did, before. Yo must know. Yo've just come out of prison. News travels well enough in there.
Louise Marshall	Whatever are you talking about?
Emily Palmer	I ain't brave like yo. I never took more than one forced feeding. After that I gave it up.
Louise Marshall	Is that it? And you've been nursing these guilty feelings all this time without a word to anyone. You old silly!
Emily Palmer	Yo ain't disgusted?
Louise Marshall	Who has taken any number of beatings and over-ridden the fear of public speaking? You may think of yourself as a coward. No one else does.
Emily Palmer	That ain't all, though. I can't believe it's right.
Louise Marshall	What . . . votes for women?

Emily Palmer   Oh, I believe in that, but not the way we does it. The violence. It's all wrong. Although, it does seem to be the only way to get what we're after. I just don't know. I'm not sure what to do any more.

Louise Marshall   Do whatever your conscience tells you, of course. There isn't one way only. If peaceful protests are right for you, then that is your path. Whatever you do, you needn't ever feel alone, not for one minute. There are hordes of us, massed together, all with the same goal, all comrades, and that is our strength.

> *The lights dim.* **Emily** *and* **Louise** *'freeze' for a moment to show time passing.*
>
> *Enter* **Peter.**

Peter Marshall   She's awake then?

Louise Marshall   Yes. The doctor says she shouldn't be disturbed, though.

Peter Marshall   I'll go then, now I know the patient's making a recovery.

Emily Palmer   No, please let him stay.

Louise Marshall   Just for a little while, then.

Emily Palmer   Thank yo for the flowers.

Peter Marshall   That's quite all right.

Emily Palmer   And for bringing me home.

Peter Marshall   Couldn't leave you to the police horses, could I? Besides, I've got a job for you . . . when you're up and well of course.

Louise Marshall   Pete, whatever are you talking about?

Peter Marshall   I haven't had much time since Father died. So much business to deal with. But things should ease off pretty soon and when they do I need someone to go up in a balloon with me. What about it, Emily?

Louise Marshall   For goodness sake, Pete!

Emily Palmer	I'll try anything once.
Peter Marshall	There you are. I knew she was the pioneering type. It'll be a last fling.
Louise Marshall	What do you mean, 'a last fling'?
Peter Marshall	When the war starts we shan't be able to fly balloons. Might drift across the Channel.
Louise Marshall	War. What war? You don't mean to tell me you believe all that stuff in the papers?
Peter Marshall	Of course I do.
Louise Marshall	Oh Peter, really! You're disturbing Emily. I really think you ought to go.
Peter Marshall	All right then. I'll be off. I'll be back tomorrow.
Emily Palmer	Peter . . .
Peter Marshall	Yes.
Emily Palmer	Yo meant that . . . about going in a balloon.
Peter Marshall	Yes. Did you think I was fooling?
Emily Palmer	I just wanted to make sure.
Peter Marshall	And you'll come?
Emily Palmer	Yes. *(Pause)* Please.

• •

Scene Thirteen

Emily and Peter sit in a large basket in the centre of the stage, if possible suspended from above.

Peter Marshall	Emily, you've got your eyes shut. You aren't scared, are you?

Emily Palmer	Bloody petrified!

He puts his arm around her.

Peter Marshall	Old goose! Come on. You can open them. It's not so bad.
Emily Palmer	*(Opening her eyes)* Why aren't we moving?
Peter Marshall	Look down!
Emily Palmer	*(Looking cautiously over the side)* It's such a long way. We must be miles over London!
Peter Marshall	About three hundred feet.
Emily Palmer	Will yo close your eyes for a moment?
Peter Marshall	Why?
Emily Palmer	I've brought some of Louise's leaflets to throw down.
Peter Marshall	Where are they?
Emily Palmer	In my bloomers.
Peter Marshall	You really are one in a million!
Emily Palmer	Close your eyes.
Peter Marshall	All right.

He covers his face. She hitches up her skirt and takes the leaflets out.

Emily Palmer	Yo can look now. Here they are.
Peter Marshall	A true suffragette!
Emily Palmer	Do you mind?
Peter Marshall	I'd hoped you might have come for the fun of it.

Emily Palmer	What, up in the sky in a basket, for the fun of it? Wild horses wouldn't have dragged me. Only I was ashamed. Not being able to stand it in prison. Betraying them all. I had to do something that took all my courage.
Peter Marshall	I see.
Emily Palmer	Something that wasn't violent.
Peter Marshall	I think yo've more courage than anyone I know. *(He takes her hand)* Emily.
Emily Palmer	What?
Peter Marshall	You're so . . . If it wasn't for the war.
Emily Palmer	What do yo mean about the war?
Peter Marshall	Just that it's inevitable.
Emily Palmer	Nonsense!
Peter Marshall	It isn't nonsense, you know. I don't suppose it will last long, but there are bound to be dangers. *(Haltingly)* And it's because of those dangers I can't say more than I hope we'll always be friends. You are such a splendid girl, so full of courage . . . a chap couldn't ask for a better companion. If only I could see into the future and be sure of coming through safely, I would . . . We can be friends, can't we?
Emily Palmer	For always, no matter what happens.
	He puts his arms around her and kisses her.
Emily Palmer	What about these leaflets, then?
Peter Marshall	Let's throw them over now.
	They throw the leaflets over the side of the basket and over the audience.
	The lights go down.

Activities

The Suffragettes   72
Prison Diary   78
Women Today   82
Making a Protest   83
Drama Ideas   86
Peter and Emily   88
What the Adaptors Say   90
Designing a Set   91
A Question of Courage on Stage   92

The Suffragettes

Louise Marshall   There are women all over England banding together in a variety
                        of groups to fight this injustice.

Read   During 1912, when Emily hears Louise speaking at the meeting in Mrs
                        Boddington's house, she suddenly realizes how unfair things are for
                        women. Women eventually managed to win the right to vote as this
                        account explains.

                        At the beginning of the nineteenth century, only rich men had the
                        right to vote. By 1884, about five million men had been given this
                        right, leaving only the poorest without a vote. But still, in 1900, hardly
                        a single woman had ever been given this right.

                        By this time some women were no longer happy to accept their
                        situation.

                        Three years earlier an organization called the National Union of
                        Women's Suffrage Societies, (NUWSS), was formed to promote the aims
                        of women and win them the vote. The women who belonged to this
                        organization were known as 'suffragists'. (*Suffrage* is the right of voting.)

                        The WSPU (Women's Social and Political Union) became known as the
                        'suffragettes' after the *Daily Mail* gave them this name. They
                        campaigned much more strongly than the NUWSS. They adopted the
                        slogan 'Deeds not words'.

                        After 1901, over twenty new suffrage societies grew up to represent
                        women's needs.

                        Between 1907 and 1910 the WSPU began deliberately to vandalise
                        private and commercial property in the hope that the publicity this
                        would attract would help their cause.

                        In 1908, there was a number of huge demonstrations and processions
                        in London as hundreds of thousands of women took to the streets to
                        demonstrate for their rights.

                        The women carried huge banners in the colours of purple, white and
                        green: the colours of the movement.

Suffragette rally in Hyde Park,
21st June 1908

These demonstrations became more and more violent, often involving clashes with the police and the arrests of several women. The *Daily Sketch* described one demonstration at this time:

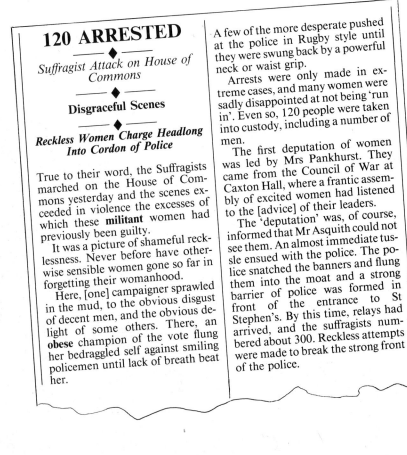

120 ARRESTED

◆

Suffragist Attack on House of Commons

◆

Disgraceful Scenes

◆

Reckless Women Charge Headlong Into Cordon of Police

True to their word, the Suffragists marched on the House of Commons yesterday and the scenes exceeded in violence the excesses of which these **militant** women had previously been guilty.

It was a picture of shameful recklessness. Never before have otherwise sensible women gone so far in forgetting their womanhood.

Here, [one] campaigner sprawled in the mud, to the obvious disgust of decent men, and the obvious delight of some others. There, an **obese** champion of the vote flung her bedraggled self against smiling policemen until lack of breath beat her.

A few of the more desperate pushed at the police in Rugby style until they were swung back by a powerful neck or waist grip.

Arrests were only made in extreme cases, and many women were sadly disappointed at not being 'run in'. Even so, 120 people were taken into custody, including a number of men.

The first deputation of women was led by Mrs Pankhurst. They came from the Council of War at Caxton Hall, where a frantic assembly of excited women had listened to the [advice] of their leaders.

The 'deputation' was, of course, informed that Mr Asquith could not see them. An almost immediate tussle ensued with the police. The police snatched the banners and flung them into the moat and a strong barrier of police was formed in front of the entrance to St Stephen's. By this time, relays had arrived, and the suffragists numbered about 300. Reckless attempts were made to break the strong front of the police.

In 1909 a woman who had been arrested and put into prison refused to eat any food and threatened to die as a way of protesting against the government. This was called a *hunger strike*. To begin with, hunger-strikers were released from prison because the government was afraid of the bad publicity their deaths would attract. Later these women were kept in prison and force-fed.

Between 1910 and 1912 there were attempts in Parliament to give women the vote, but these were opposed by the majority of men.

In 1913, the Cat and Mouse Act was brought in to respond to the public outcry at the force-feeding of women. The Act allowed women who were ill through lack of food to be released from prison and then readmitted later if necessary.

In the same year there was the most famous protest of all when Emily Davison died after deliberately running in front of the King's horse at the Derby.

In August 1914, as Europe moved towards a World War, Mrs Pankhurst ordered her members to stop all their action in the face of a challenge to the freedom of men and women.

Talk

SUFFRAGETTE ORGANISATIONS

VANDALISING OF PROPERTY

PROTEST   SUFFRAGETTE ARRESTS

FORCE-FEEDING   WORLD WAR ONE

In groups, answer these questions.

1   Which of the headings above describes events which happen in **A Question of Courage?** For each one, make a note of

  • the scene

  • which characters are involved

  • what happens in the play.

2   Make a list of all the characters in the play who are actively involved in trying to win the vote for women.

3   Which of these characters do you feel most sympathy for or closest to? Explain your answer.

4   Re-read the extract from the *Daily Sketch*.
    Whose point of view do you think it is written from?
    Which words suggest this? List them.

5   How would it have appeared to Louise or Emily if they had been involved in this particular protest?
    Imagine one of them is being interviewed by the *Daily Sketch* reporter who wrote the article. In pairs, act out what she might have said to the reporter.

Write

Choose three characters in the play. For each one, select one day on which something important happens. Imagine you are the character. Write a diary for each of the three days.

For example, if you choose Emily Palmer, you might select the day she gets her bicycle or the night when she is caught on the golf-course with Louise Marshall.

Research

Find out more about women's struggle to win the vote. When did they finally achieve equal voting rights? Why do you think it took such a long time?

PRISON EXPERIENCES OF LADY CONSTANCE LYTTON.

FORCIBLE FEEDING IN PRISON.

In some cases, instead of nasal feeding as in the picture, the still more dangerous practice of feeding through the mouth, by a tube, down the throat, is adopted. This was done in the case of Jane Warton.

Prison Diary

In July 1909, Gladys Roberts, a solicitor's clerk from Leeds, was sentenced to one month's imprisonment for throwing stones at windows during a suffragette protest. While she was in prison, she went on hunger-strike. She kept a diary in shorthand, which describes her experiences.

Wednesday, July 14.

We were all taken down separately. My bag and hat were taken from me by six wardresses. I told the magistrates I was not sorry for breaking windows, and that I did not intend to comply with any second-division rules, so was sentenced to seven days' close confinement, and was brought down to this cell, with nothing in it except a block of wood fixed to the wall for a chair and a plank bed and pillow . . . unbreakable opaque windows, and double iron doors—God help me to stick it! I can hear the others singing, thank goodness!

They have brought us a pint of cocoa and a lump of the usual bread. Hunger strike commences. The drum and fife band is coming at eight o'clock. I wonder if we shall hear it. We seem to be buried alive.

Thursday, July 15.

I heard a bell this morning so I dressed. Wardresses came. 'Any applications?' I asked for the governor and the doctor. I lie on the bed —I feel so weak—breakfast has just been put in. I said I didn't want any. God help me! I wonder if those outside are thinking about us. I am a coward. A day of reckoning will come for this Government. No sunshine can get into this cell and at night there is a gas jet burning over the door. Always a dull light. However, my room at Stamford and Metcalfe where I sat for four years was not much lighter than this.

I have seen the doctor. He argued with me about the unreasonableness of our conduct . . . The chaplain came. He was rather nice. He asked if there was anything I wanted. I said I wanted a good many things, and I supposed we would not be allowed a library book . . . He said he was very sorry to see us here, and I couldn't keep back a few tears when he had gone. I feel so weak. A wardress brought in a Bible, Prayer Book and Hymn Book. I read the marriage service over. I thought it would get my blood up, so I read Paul's opinion on the duties of a wife.

I suppose Mother and Father are enjoying the sea air at Bridlington. Thank God they don't know where I am. The bang of the double doors is terrible. It seems strange to think of all whom we love going about their business in the normal way while we—Oh, I do feel blubbery. I expect it's because I'm losing my strength. I'm not usually given to weeping, but I feel I should like to have a jolly good cry.

I hear knocking on the walls, and all the prisoners are shouting that they have not eaten their food. Neither have I. Dinner consisted of an egg and potatoes and a pint of milk and (oh, awful temptation!) a boiled onion. I am getting disinclined to write even.

The governor's been. I asked if yesterday's proceedings were to be considered as Herbert Gladstone's reply. He said that the visiting magistrates were a separate body, and acted on their own initiative. Herbert Gladstone had not replied. I expect the visiting magistrates get their orders from Gladstone as I saw my sentence was written down before I was tried.

Friday, July 16.

The wardress said to me this morning, 'Get your clothes on. We shall want to take your bed out.' I wonder if they will. Miss Carwin didn't have hers all day yesterday. Part of the process seems to be to degrade us by not allowing us to wash properly. This morning I have had only my drinking can of water to wash in. May Gladstone's downfall be speedy!

. . . I saw through the peephole, which was accidentally left open, Mrs Holtwhite Simmons go out of the cell opposite looking ghastly. I wonder if I look likewise. Fifty-four hours without food! God help me to hold out! I feel so choky when I think of the world outside.

Saturday, July 17.

I can't get up this morning. The cleaner came and swept out my cell. She smiled at me and it made me so weepy. The doctor has been and tried to persuade me to give up the hunger strike by saying that I was not so robust as the others. What would my mother and father say, and so on. I had to make a fool of myself after he had gone.

It is now seventy-two hours since I tasted food. The governor and matron have just been to say that Herbert Gladstone had written that he has fully considered the petitions, but sees no reason why he should take action in the matter which proves he could, if he would.

Tremendous excitement—Mary Allen has just come down to the cell next to mine. She broke more windows when she heard Herbert Gladstone's reply. It has quite bucked me up.

There has been a butterfly in my cell all day. It beat itself against the window all night and made such a noise until I got up and put it in a paper bag.

Sunday, July 18.

Had a fairly good night, but dreaming of food all the time. I feel more cheerful today. I've had quite long talks with Mary Allen through the wall. We've beaten Miss Wallace Dunlop's record! Dinner time today will be ninety-six hours without food . . .

Monday, July 19.

I had rather a bad night. The bed, I was sure, must be stuffed with stones, and my poor bones ached terribly. At a little after twelve o'clock, just after dinner had been thrust in, the hospital matron and two prisoners with a carrying chair came for me and carried me to the hospital. They put me to bed and gave me a hot-water bottle and brought me jelly, milk, and bread and butter, which of course I refused. The doctor came and talked and talked, but I wouldn't budge. Then he came and asked me where I wanted what was left of me to be sent at the end of the month. I said I did not think that there would be any to send anywhere. I gave him Clement's Inn and Miss Jones's address.

At 6.20, the governor came with the matron and said: 'Are you feeling miserable?' I said: 'Not at all, I'm very comfortable.' He said: 'Are you still obstinate?' 'Yes.' 'Well, I have some news for you—you are to be released.'

He told me to be very quiet and move about slowly, and he would send a wardress to dress me and also some brandy in a beaten egg. He said he would send to Miss Jones and see if she could take me. As soon as he had gone, I got up and waited, and at about 7.20, after the matron had brought my bag, a wardress came for me and I was taken in a cab to the Joneses.

At about eight o'clock, the drum and fife band came, and they fetched Mrs Leigh in to see me, and then Mrs Lawrence and Christabel came just as I was put to bed. I was never so happy in my life.

Read

Look up the meanings of any difficult words you do not understand in these diary entires.

Talk

Have you ever been really hungry? Describe any time you can remember when, for some reason, you had to go without food. How did it feel? Would you be prepared to go on a hunger-strike for anything?

Write

If Emily Palmer had kept a diary while she was in Holloway Prison, what do you think she would have written? Write a few extracts from her diary.

or

Write an extract from the diary of a female prison warder. Do you believe that women should have the vote? How do you feel about force-feeding prisoners? If you were asked to do it as part of your job, would you?

Act

In pairs, improvise one or more scenes based on Gladys Roberts' diary. One of you could play Gladys, the other could play the doctor, the prison chaplain or the prison governor. Re-read the extracts from the diary to find out what your character's attitude is. (Does your character sympathise with Gladys? Do you try to make her abandon her hunger-strike?)

Women Today

Read

In a **A Question of Courage,** we can see how a number of women fought to win the vote. In this struggle they were only asking to be treated as equals with men who already had this right. Some people think that, although today all women can vote, they have not yet become truly equal with men.

Talk

In pairs, look at these statements carefully.

Decide which, if any of them, you agree with. Write some statements of your own.

- Girls are more intelligent than boys.
- Girls are not as active as boys.
- There aren't many female Members of Parliament because women don't enjoy politics.
- There are too many men in Parliament.
- There would be more female Members of Parliament if men looked after the children.
- Women should use the vote which was won for them.
- Women should use their vote for other women.
- Women don't give other women enough political support.

Compare the statements you agree with with those of another pair.

In groups, discuss:

Are boys and girls treated equally in your school?

In your home?

Give as many practical examples to back up your arguments as you can.

Making a Protest

Louise Marshall   We need action if we're ever going to get the Vote. People take notice of action, especially drastic action.

Talk   There is a photograph on page 75 of one of the most famous protests by a woman seeking to win the Vote. Another famous protest involved women chaining themselves to the railings of Buckingham Palace.

In pairs

1   Make a list of all the different protests in the play.

2   Which of these do you think was the most 'drastic' and the most effective? Why?

3   Which of these would you have been prepared to make if you had been a woman living at the start of this century?

Read   Since the time of this play, young people have protested over a number of issues. Study the photographs on pages 84 and 85 and find out what they were protesting for or against.

Think   What would you be prepared to demonstrate for? Would you be prepared to be violent?

What would you do . . .

• if a friend was punished at school for something she or he did not do?

• if someone you knew was sent to prison wrongly?

• if a teacher you liked was treated unfairly?

• if your school was closed down, although everyone wanted it to stay open?

Write

Making a protest

In pairs or small groups do a survey on members of your class to find out:

- what is most important to them

- what they would be willing to protest for

- what kinds of protest they would make

Stage 1 Prepare a questionnaire to ask your friends these questions.
Stage 2 Carry out the survey.
Stage 3 Present your results in some kind of chart.
Stage 4 Write a short piece in which you present your view on this subject.
Stage 5 Present all this information to show other students in your school.

Drama Ideas

Warm-up ideas

1 Thirty Second protests

Think of a subject about which you could protest.

For example:

- better food in your school canteen

- no school uniform

- new zebra crossing near your school

- more money spent on the school library

Work out three or four good points to support your case. Speak for thirty seconds without stopping.

Think of an unusual way of protesting, suitable to your chosen subject, and do it!

2 Frozen moments

In groups, choose the three moments in **A Question of Courage** that most stick in your mind. Imagine you are going to 'freeze' the action of each scene, as if it was a photograph.

Draw up your three 'frozen moments'. Try and make sure each scene is as exciting as possible to look at, with what is going on shown very clearly.

Longer Activities

1 A woman's place — 1912

Imagine that you are a member of the Ladies' Guild during the year 1912. Because of the protests and demonstrations taking place over the issue of the right of women to vote, your group has been talking about this subject. There are many different views represented in your Guild. Some women think that the protests are a disgrace; some that they are a very good thing. Some of your group are not quite sure what they think, or at least are afraid of speaking up in public in case their husbands find out.

Your have decided to prepare a number of short plays to present to the next meeting of the group. The title of these plays will be 'A Woman's Place'.

In groups of four to six, prepare two short plays for the Ladies Guild.

One should show a woman who has a very unusual place in her home. She might be a campaigner for women's rights, for example. The other should show a much more traditional picture of a woman's place.

Perform the plays to the rest of the class. If you can, find out what clothes were being worn in 1912 and dress up for your parts.

2   A woman's place today

In groups, prepare and act a brief play in which you show your views of what a woman's place should be in today's world.

3   The WSPU

Imagine you are a girl or boy of your own age living at the time of **A Question of Courage.** You have just been to hear a speaker called Louise Marshall tell a large crowd of people that women should start to take action to change their lives.

You are so impressed that you have decided to join the WSPU, or if you are a boy, to find some way, like Peter in the play, of supporting women in their struggle.

In groups, prepare the scene in which you tell your parents and family about your decision. Think carefully about how they might react.

4   Force-feeding

In pairs, imagine how you would have reacted as father and mother of someone who has just been put into prison and force-fed. Choose interesting characters for yourself. For example, one of you could be an important politician who is becoming sympathetic to the women's fight for equality. You might be someone who has always worked at home and just joined one of the organizations fighting to gain the Vote.

Have an argument with your partner about whether or not force-feeding should be allowed.

Peter and Emily

Peter Marshall   And it's because of these dangers I can't say more than I hope we'll always be friends.

Talk

How do Peter and Emily first meet? What do you think is going through her mind? What does he think of her?

Role Play

Reread Act One, Scene Six. What do you think Louise, Peter and Emily would have talked about in the car? In threes, roleplay this scene. Before you do this, decide what you think the mood of each of the characters would have been.

In the play Emily gets into trouble when she returns home from her unexpected meeting with Louise and Peter. Her father shouts at her and she is forced to run out of the kitchen. In pairs, improvise a scene that follows in which Emily tells May, who has followed her out, what has just happened.

Remember that she would have very mixed feelings after having the bicycle she had been saving up for damaged so soon after she had collected it!

Hot Seating

Hot seating is a way of finding out what is in a character's mind. When you have played a role or acted out a part you can be put 'in the hot seat'. This means that the person playing the character is asked questions by others in the group and then answers as if he/she were actually that character.

Put Emily in the hot seat. Find out what she is really thinking when she returns home, after she has talked to May, about,

- her family
- the meeting
- her bicycle
- Peter and Louise.

Talk

1   What does Peter do to help Emily, Louise and the women's cause in the play? Make a list of everything he does. What does he do to help Emily in particular?

2   What do you think Emily and Peter were thinking at the end of the play? Do you think they were in love with each other?

Act

In pairs, act out the last scene of the play. Try out different ways of playing the two characters. Try showing them,

*   very much in love

*   not in love, but having a real friendship

*   some other way.

Write

What happened next?

Continue the play.

Either continue the play as a story or a play. Decide what happened in the coming years, considering all you know about the characters and the First World War.

Or imagine that after their balloon ride, Emily and Peter go their separate ways. Each one is thinking of the other. Write an exchange of four letters between them in which you bring out their feelings for each other and their plans for the future.

What the Adaptors Say

We have always admired Marjorie Darke's writing and thought **A Question of Courage** would make a very good play for young people.

We particularly liked the fact that we could include so many characters in our version of the novel. There should be enough parts for most readers in a class to have an individual part.

If you know the novel you will notice a number of changes that we decided to make. We wanted to keep the main focus of the play very much on Emily Palmer, on her relationship with Louise and, later, on her feelings for Peter. Emily also begins to have doubts about the violence used in the struggle and about how brave she herself has been. All of this we felt would give a young actress plenty to work on.

Because of this interest in Emily we had to cut out much of the more detailed description of Emily's family and the tensions within it.

Sometimes you will see that we have moved scenes and characters so that we can keep the plot going. For example, we have changed the way in which Emily actually first obtains her bicycle.

Certain features of the novel were very difficult to solve. You can read about a car very briefly in a book but on stage it is more difficult to show cars (and bicycles!). You might like to see if you can make up a scene showing Louise and Peter setting off in the car for the meeting at Mrs Boddington's house.

Another interesting feature of the book is Marjorie Darke's very careful use of language. The way Emily and Louise speak is completely different. Each character in the novel speaks in a distinct way. We have tried to keep a flavour of this. You will see this particularly by the way some characters use the word 'yo' rather than you. You might like to try listening to the fascinating ways in which people speak in different parts of Britain and see how you would write it down.

Above all, we hope that you will enjoy this and, if you act it out, try to keep it moving along. You might want to assemble some simple objects from the First World War period to suggest scenes, rather than trying to do complicated scene changes.

We were particularly pleased when Marjorie Darke wrote to us saying that she thought it was a sensitive adaptation of her novel. We hope you think so too!

Bill Lucas and Brian Keaney

Designing a Set

Think

Study this outline plan of a stage. Make a list of all the different settings needed in the play. Decide which part of this particular design of a set you would use for each of these settings. Draw some of them out in detail.

The play is written to be performed in the classroom or on the stage. Although it has thirty parts and is, therefore, suitable for reading in class, most scenes have a much smaller number of characters and could be performed by a small group.

The play is set between 1912 and 1914 in the Midlands and in London. There are a large number of scenes with many different settings. For all of these it would be possible to have some kind of back-drop. It may be just as effective, however, to have a huge photograph of a demonstration projected onto a wall or back-drop throughout the play.

Alternatively, you could use a number of slides; or it would be very effective if no back-drop at all was used and scenes were suggested by simple props: an old-fashioned sewing-machine for the opening scene, a flag for the golf-course, a kitchen table and some kitchen utensils for the Palmer house.

The important thing is to keep the action going as fast as possible, only pausing where you feel it is important to the action of the play. Complex scene changes will stop this flow.

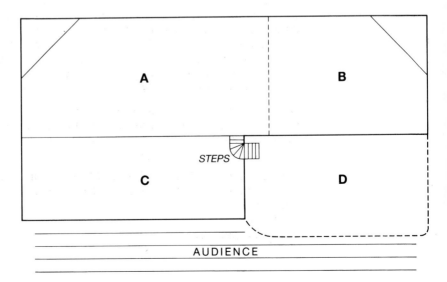

A Question of Courage on Stage

Music

Find out what music was popular at this time and try and obtain some recordings. Use them in your version of the play.

Read this verse from a protest song of the time. Sing it if you can. Make up your own words to this tune and write them out.

Shout, shout, up with your song! Cry with the wind, for the dawn is breaking.

March, march, swing you along, Wide blows our banner and hope is waking.

Song with its story, dreams with their glory, Lo! they call and glad is their word.

Forward! Hark how it swells! Thunder of freedom, the voice of the Lord!

Design

Design a large cut-out balloon, suitable for use at the end of the play, and paint it.

Make placards suitable for use by Louise, Emily, Vera and the others on their Bicycle Parade.

Find out about the fashion of the period just before the First World War. Design a poster to advertise a production of the play.

Write

Produce a programme for **A Question of Courage.** (Before you do this it would be helpful if you could assemble a number of programmes for other plays.)

Include in your programme:

- any artwork or photographs you think are appropriate

- a brief description of what the play is about

- brief notes on some of the more important characters (use the character list at the front of the play to help you).

- anything else you think would be helpful.

Act

Act out part or all of the play. You could use the props, poster and programme you have made when you do this.

The photographs on pages 84 and 85 show:

1 the Burston school strike, 1914: farm workers set up their own village school. Before this, education had been controlled by local landowners and by the church. As part of the strike, children refused to attend the 'official' school.

2 student demonstrations in Paris, 1968, against President de Gaulle's educational reforms.

3 student demonstrations in China, 1989, calling for greater democracy, general elections, and freedom of speech.

4 a demonstration in Grosvenor Square, London, in 1968. Demonstrators protested against American military intervention in Vietnam.

Acknowledgements

Prison diary extract by Gladys Roberts, p. 78, from *The Militant Suffragettes* by Antonia Raeburn (Michael Joseph, 1973). Reprinted by permission of the Peters, Fraser & Dunlop Group Ltd.

Song verse and music, 'Shout, shout, up with your song!', p. 92, from *Suffragettes and Votes for Women* by L E Snelgrove (Longman, 1964). Reprinted by permission of J. Curwen and Sons Ltd.

The publishers would like to thank the following for permission to reproduce photographs:

Barnaby's Picture Library pp. 59, 70; Birmingham Central Library p. 8; Culver Pictures Inc. p. 44; The Hulton-Deutsch Collection pp. 75, 85: The Living Archive Project, p. 84 (top); Magnum/Bruno Barbey p. 84 (bottom left),/Stuart Franklin p. 84 (bottom right); Mary Evans/Fawcett Library p. 17; Museum of London pp. 2, 27, 52, 73, 77; Radcliffe College p. 38.

Illustrations are by Peter Melnyczuk

Other plays in this series include:

Across the Barricades   ISBN 0 19 831272 5
    Joan Lingard   adapted by David Ian Neville

The Demon Headmaster   ISBN 0 19 831270 9
    Gillian Cross   adapted by Adrian Flynn

Frankenstein   ISBN 0 19 831267 9
    Mary Shelley   adapted by Philip Pullman

Paper Tigers   ISBN 0 19 831268 7
    Steve Barlow and Steve Skidmore

The Turbulent Term of Tyke Tiler   ISBN 0 19 831269 5
    adapted from her own novel by Gene Kemp

Forthcoming titles include:

The Burston School Strike   ISBN 0 19 831274 1
    Roy Nevitt

Hot Cakes   ISBN 0 19 831273 3
    Adrian Flynn

The Teen Commandments   ISBN 0 19 831275 X
    Kelvin Reynolds

Tigers on the Prowl   ISBN 0 19 831277 6
    Steve Barlow and Steve Skidmore